THE JOY OF FATHERHOOD

BY
WILLY LOHMANN

IDEAS UNLIMITED
PUBLISHING

This edition published in the U.K. by Ideas Unlimited (Publishing) P.O. Box 125, Portsmouth, Hampshire PO1 4PP

I.S.B.N. 1 871964 04 0

Cover designed by Ian Churchill

Printed in Great Britain.

First published in Netherlands by Mondria Publishers, Hazerwoude, The Netherlands.

INTRODUCTION

This is Prof. Ernst-Jan P. Broekeman, a confirmed bachelor who for many years researched and studied all aspects of fatherhood; and admits that his present status is a direct reflection of his findings.

He will guide us through a brief journey of some of these aspects. We would point out that for the benefit of some young fathers and would be fathers, the contents of this book has to a great extent been softened up to prevent a sudden change of heart, heart failure or even suicide.

PROF. DR. ERNST. JAN P. BROEKEMAN

4

THE EARLY DAYS.

THE BIRTH IS ALWAYS A NERVE-RECKING EXPERIENCE.
BUT IT'S NOTHING COMPARED TO WHAT LIES AHEAD
DON'T RELAX TOO MUCH JUST YET

BE A LITTLE SELECTIVE WHEN CHOOSING
A NAME.

LET YOUR SENSES TREASURE THOSE MOMENTS.

TREAT THE NEW BORN TO THOSE NICE FATHERLY GIFTS.

THE VISITORS.

THE RECOGNITION

FEEDING
TIMES: 8am
12am 3pm

THERE IS NOTHING SISSY ABOUT PUSHING
A PRAM. SO WALK LIKE A PROUD
DADDY. JUST DON'T FORGET THE
HAT AND THE DARK GLASSES.

SOME FATHERS GO TO GREAT LENGTHS TO PROVE
THAT THEY ARE STILL WITH IT.

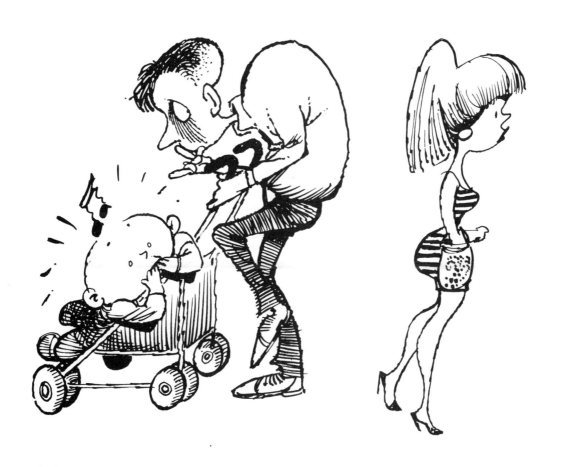

SOME CHILDREN MATURE QUICKER THAN OTHERS.

DO TRY AND ENJOY THE DAILY RITUALS.

BE PATIENT, AND REMEMBER THE HARDER IT
GOES IN THE HARDER IT COMES OUT.

A SMALL STEP ON THE WAY TO INDEPENDENCE.
A GIANT STEP ON THE WAY
TO DISASTER.

REMEMBER THAT WITH A CHILD, A GOOD NIGHTS
SLEEP IS A THING OF THE PAST.

SOME FATHERS CAN AT TIMES BE A LITTLE
TOO OVER-CAUTIOUS.

FATHER'S PRIDE

SOME FATHERS CAN AT TIMES OVER SELL THEIR
SON'S ABILITY

AND THE CHILDREN IN TURN LEARN QUICKLY
TO FOLLOW IN THEIR DAD'S FOOTSTEPS.

PLAYING IS LEARNING.

TRY AND BE ENCOURAGING AT ALL TIMES.

THERE WILL COME A TIME WHEN YOU FIND THAT THE
CHILD COULD DO WITH A LITTLE ADVICE

SOMETIMES THEIR IMAGINATION COULD
TURN OUT TO BE A PAIN IN THE NECK.

TRY AND TAKE PART IN THEIR GAMES.

STAY ENTHUSIASTIC

ENCOURAGE YOUR CHILD'S CREATIVE TENDANCIES

A GOOD CHAT SOMETIMES DOES WONDERS.

TRY AND BE AS DISCREET AS POSSIBLE
WHEN MAKING THE HOME VIDEO OF YOUR CHILD.

SOME GAMES NEVER DATE.

FATHER, CHILD
& PET

TELL YOUR SON THAT EVERY ANIMAL HAS ITS LIMITATIONS.

EDUCATING IS A SKILL.

MAKE SURE THE CHILD PSYCHOLOGY BOOK IS ALWAYS
AT HAND.

TRY TO NIP BAD HABBITS IN THE BUD.

SETTING AN EXAMPLE IS AN ESSENTIAL
PART OF FATHERHOOD.

DON'T EVER CHOOSE THE EASY WAY OUT.

THERE JUST MIGHT BE A BETTER WAY.

CHOOSE YOUR ARGUMENTS VERY CAREFULLY.

SOMETIMES PUNISHMENT BECOMES INEVITABLE.

TRY NOT TO PULL THE SAME EAR
EVERY TIME.

DR. SPOCK'S MANUAL CAN BE
VERY HANDY AT TIMES.

MUSIC

A LITTLE ENCOURAGEMENT, PARTICULARLY
IN THE BEGINNING MAY, BECOME
NECESSARY.

CHOOSE YOUR CHILD'S INSTRUMENT WITH CARE.

DO NOT TRUST THE SO CALLED FRIEND OR RELATIVE
WHO GIVES YOUR SON A DRUM KIT.

CHILDREN ARE
INQUISITIVE

CURIOSITY AND BUSINESS SENSE CAN GO
HAND IN HAND.

CURIOSITY CAN ALSO BE JUST TECHNICAL.

A CHILD'S PERCEPTION OF THE WORLD CAN
DIFFER FROM THAT OF HIS FATHER'S.

THE CHILD'S INTEREST CAN BE VERY UNPREDICTABLE.

A CHILD GROWS UP QUICKER THAN YOU THINK.

THE CHILD'S ROOM OFTEN SPEAKS VOLUMES.

THINK CAREFULLY BEFORE OFFERING TO DO YOUR
CHILD'S HOMEWORK.

A VISIT TO THE SCHOOL CAN BE VERY EYE-OPENING.

WHEN YOU BUY CLOTHES FOR YOUR
CHILD, ALWAYS ALLOW FOR GROWING.

THERE WILL COME A TIME WHEN YOUR DAUGHTER
DISCOVERS THE JOY OF USING THE TELEPHONE.

DON'T BE ASHAMED TO TURN TO OTHERS
FOR SUPPORT.

OTHER TITLES AVAILABLE FROM IDEAS UNLIMITED (PUBLISHING).

Please send me:

☐ copy / copies of **"100 Chat Up Lines"** ISBN 1-871964-00-8 (128 pages A7)   **@ £1.99** (postage free)

☐ copy / copies of **"Of course I Love You"** ISBN 1-871964-01-6 (96 pages A6)   **@ £1.99** (postage free)

☐ copy / copies of **"The Beginners Guide to Kissing"** ISBN 1-871964-02-4 (64 pages A5)   **@ £2.50** (postage free)

☐ copy / copies of **"Tips for a Successful Marriage"** ISBN 1-871964-03-2 (64 pages A5)   **@ £2.50** (postage free)

☐ copy / copies of **"The Joy of Fatherhood"** ISBN 1-871964-04-0 (64 pages A5)   **@ £2.50** (postage free)

☐ copy / copies of **"Office Hanky Panky"** ISBN 1-871964-05-9 (64 pages A5)   **@ £2.50** (postage free)

I Have enclosed a cheque / postal order for £.......................... made payable to Ideas Unlimited (Publishing)

Name: ....

Address: ....

Fill in the coupon and send it with your payment to: **Ideas Unlimited (Publishing) PO Box 125, Portsmouth PO1 4PP**